Dre Snate

by Jane A C West & Roger Hurn

Illustrated by Anthony Williams

HEVER C.E.
PRIMARY
SCHOOL

Titles in Alien Detective Agency

Renegade Robots	Roger Hurn/Jane A C West
Deep Space Dinosaur Disaster	Roger Hurn/Jane A C West
Comet Riders	Roger Hurn/Jane A C West
Clowns in Town	Roger Hurn/Jane A C West
World Cup Chaos	Roger Hurn/Jane A C West
Special FX	Jane A C West/Roger Hurn
Mirror, Mirror	Jane A C West/Roger Hurn
Shadows from Beyond the Stars	Jane A C West/Roger Hurn
Looking After Wolmump	Jane A C West/Roger Hurn
Dream Snatcher	Jane A C West/Roger Hurn

Badger Publishing Limited
Suite G08,
Stevenage, Hertfordshire SG1 2DX
Telephone: 01438 791 037
Fax: 01438 791 036
www.badgerlearning.co.uk

Dream Snatcher ISBN 978-1-84926-622-2

Text © Jane A C West/Roger Hurn 2012
Complete work © Badger Publishing Limited 2012

Publisher: Susan Ross
Senior Editor: Danny Pearson
Design: Julia King
Illustration: Anthony Williams

Dream Snatcher

Contents

Vocabulary:

Alien Forums – an online network for aliens to moan about humans

encyclopaedia –
a book of information about lots of things (in alphabetical order)

Titan – powerful creatures from Greek mythology; also the name of the deepest cave in Britain

Main characters:

Jack Swift – the star of a top rated TV show

Wanda Darkstar –
the Galactic Union's Alien Welfare Officer for Earth.

Hypnos/the Dream Snatcher –
an alien who steals dreams

Chapter 1

Bad dreams

Wanda woke up feeling grumpy.

She'd had a bad dream. Jack had crashed his spaceship and they were both stuck on the planet Pluto in the middle of an icy winter.

Jack was her partner in the Alien Detective Agency.

He was also a TV star on Earth.

He never let her forget that bit.

Wanda's main job was to make sure the aliens who lived on Earth stayed hidden from humans.

But when she checked the Alien Forums that morning, they were all very grumpy.

Wanda was good at maths and this sum was pretty easy: grumpy aliens = T.R.O.U.B.L.E.

She found Jack at the TV studio working on his hit show, 'Sci-Fi Spy Guy'.

"You look fed up," he said.

"I think we've got a problem with the aliens on Earth," said Wanda.

Jack looked serious. "What's up?"

"I'm not sure," said Wanda. "All the aliens are really grumpy – I think something bad is going to happen."

Suddenly all the light bulbs in the TV studio went out.

"I hate it when you're right..." said Jack.

But he was asleep before he finished his sentence. So was everyone else.

Wanda dreamed that she was being chased by a giant, slimy alien.

Jack dreamed all his fans boo-ed him.

Wanda dreamed she was about to be covered in slime. She forced herself to wake up.

She looked around her. Everyone in the dark TV studio was having bad dreams, too. When Jack screamed, everyone woke up.

"What's going on?" said Jack, crossly.

"We're all having nightmares," said Wanda.

"But why?" asked Jack.

"I think," said Wanda, "someone – or something – is stealing our dreams!"

Chapter 2
Mega bites

Jack looked worried. "How can someone steal our dreams?" he said. "And why?"

Wanda shook her head. This maths sum was harder: two good questions = two bad answers. "I don't know," she said, "but we have to find out."

"Let's ask the computer on STEALTH," said Jack.

STEALTH was Jack's spaceship: the Space Tripping Extra Atomic Laser Time Hopper.

"Go away," said STEALTH.

Jack looked amazed. His computer had never told him to go away before.

"Do you know who is stealing our dreams?" asked Jack.

"Go away," said STEALTH again.

"I think your computer is feeling grumpy," whispered Wanda.

"Don't be daft!" said Jack. "Computers don't have feelings."

"Is that right, Mr Know-it-all!" said STEALTH. "Well you can just push off and work it out for yourself for a change. I'm fed up with being taken for granted."

STEALTH turned itself off and wouldn't talk any more.

"I think you've upset it," said Wanda.

Jack's mouth was so wide open he nearly tripped over it.

"What's going on?" he said.

"My guess is that STEALTH is having bad dreams, too," said Wanda. "We've got to find out which alien can steal dreams."

"How will we do that now STEALTH won't talk to us?" asked Jack.

"We do it the old way," said Wanda.

Jack looked puzzled.

"We look in a book," said Wanda.

Chapter 3

A regular page turner

"Wow! These books are cool!" said Jack.

Wanda had a whole library of books on aliens. There were Icylons from an ice planet, slime monsters from Planet Swamp and blood-sucking vampire aliens from Planet Drac.

"I had an en**cyclo**paedia once," said Jack.

"What happened to it?" asked Wanda.

"I preferred walking," he said.

Wanda rolled her eyes. Jack's jokes didn't get any better.

Jack picked up one of Wanda's books. It was huge, heavy and had a lock on the front.

"This looks really old," said Jack.

"It is," said Wanda. "Aliens have been visiting Earth for thousands of years. It's a popular place for family holidays."

Jack didn't know if she was joking. She didn't look like she was joking, but sometimes it was hard to tell.

He flipped through some pages. There was a picture of a man dressed like a Roman soldier.

The picture showed the soldier was having a bad nightmare.

"I think I've found it," said Jack. "Look at this. It says that the alien called Hypnos is a Dream Snatcher. It feeds on the energy from dreams. Wow! That's a big alien!"

Wanda came to read over his shoulder.

"You're right," she said. "But this book says Hypnos doesn't stay on Earth very long and doesn't steal more than one dream at a time. So what has changed?"

"Yes," said Jack, "and why is it giving so many people nightmares instead?"

Chapter 4
Titan's cave

"What do we do now?" said Jack.

"We have to catch the Dream Snatcher before night time," said Wanda. "If we don't, there will be a lot of people having very bad nightmares."

Jack looked at the sky.

"We've only got a couple of hours till sunset," he said.

Wanda looked grim.

"Then we'd better get busy," she said.

"Where will we find Hypnos?" said Jack.

Wanda pointed to the book. "It says here that Hypnos likes to live in a cave. All we have to do is find the right cave... but there must be thousands near here."

Jack began to smile.

"What's so funny?" said Wanda crossly.

"I've just had an idea," said Jack. "You know you said aliens come to Earth all the time for holidays?"

"Yes, so?" said Wanda.

"And the Dream Snatcher is really big?" said Jack.

"Yes, so?" said Wanda impatiently.

"Well," said Jack, "the deepest cave in Britain is called Titan. And in ancient myths, Titan means..."

"Giant monster!" finished Wanda. She looked impressed. "So where is this monster cave?"

"Derbyshire," said Jack. "We're going to need your hover-scooter. Can I drive?"

"On your bike!" said Wanda.

Chapter 5

Deep down

Wanda's hover-scooter sailed through the clouds.

It was cold and wet and not much fun, decided Jack. Worse still, the sun was setting. Soon people all over Britain would be falling asleep – and dreaming.

"There it is!" shouted Jack.

The cave opening was like a giant mouth – sharp stones hung down like teeth.

They tiptoed into the cave. The rocky floor led them down, down into the dark.

"I forgot to say," whispered Wanda. "Whatever you do, don't fall asleep!"

It was too late. Jack was lying on the cave floor snoring loudly.

"Uh-oh!" said Wanda. "I must... stay... awake... must.... zzz."

She dreamed the slime monster was oozing all over her hair.

"Nooo!" she yelled.

Her shout woke them up.

"Oi!" yelled Jack. "What's the big idea, Mr Dream Snatcher? That's the worst nightmare I've ever had! My TV show has not been axed!"

From out of the gloom, came three huge, staring eyes, shining like lamps.

"Ssssleeeep!" said a deep voice. "Ssssleeep!"

"No!" said Wanda crossly. "No more bad dreams!"

The eyes blinked.

"Just a little dream," said Hypnos. "I need your dreams!"

"What for?" asked Wanda, "And why give us bad ones instead?"

Hypnos looked surprised. "Oh, sssorry! I didn't know I was doing that. It's just that I'm ssso unhappy. My ssspaceship is broken. I need a huge burssst of energy to fix it – if I can't fix it, I can't fly home. And... I'm ssso lonely."

Jack and Wanda felt sorry for the Dream Snatcher. But they couldn't let him give everyone else bad nightmares.

Then Jack had one of his ideas. "If I take you somewhere you can get a load of dreams in one go, will you promise not to give everyone nightmares?"

Chapter 6

A class act

It was morning. They had hidden Hypnos in an empty building site nearby.

"What are we doing here?" asked Wanda.

Jack smiled. "It's my old school."

"How is this going to help?" said Wanda.

"Well," said Jack. "It's Monday."

"So?" said Wanda, puzzled.

Jack explained. "Everyone falls asleep in assembly on Monday morning – especially when Mr Jones is telling one of his un-funny stories. There should be enough dream power to send Hypnos home."

Wanda grinned. "You're brighter than you look, Jack! Let's hope this works."

The first bell rang and children ran in from the playground.

"In ten minutes," said Jack, "everyone will be asleep."

They peered through the window of the school hall.

Soon the children were dozing and even the teachers were nodding off.

Wanda pinched herself to stay awake and elbowed Jack in the ribs. "It's working!" she hissed.

A blue light was shining from the building site. They could hear the sound of spaceship engines.

Suddenly the Dream Snatcher's
spaceship shot out of the building site.

The noise woke everyone up.

"Oh, thank goodness," said Mr Jones
with a shudder. "I dreamed the summer
holidays had been cancelled!"

"Now that really is a nightmare!" said
Jack.

Facts about dreams

We all dream every night, but we don't always remember them.

Dreams can last for a few seconds or as long as 20 minutes.

Dreams happen when our brain is very busy when we're asleep.

Some people think our dreams tell us about what is going to happen in the future.

A scientist studied 50,000 dreams from people in different countries. He said that people all over the world dream the same sort of dreams.

Most people dream in colour, but some people only dream in black and white.

Animals dream. Dogs, cats and other animals have been seen chewing, running, barking or crying while they sleep.

People who were born blind don't 'see' their dreams although they can hear, touch, taste and even smell in dreams. People who became blind later still 'see' in their dreams.

The poet Samuel Taylor Coleridge wrote his famous poem 'Kubla Khan' after he dreamed it.

The writer Robert Louis Stevenson came up with the story of 'Dr Jekyll and Mr Hyde' while he was dreaming.

Jack's joke

What did the Dream Snatcher's mum say when he finally got home?

Where on Earth have you been?

Questions

What was Wanda's first nightmare about?

What was Jack's second nightmare about?

What was the Dream Snatcher's name?

Where did the Dream Snatcher go on holiday?

How long does Wanda say aliens have been visiting Earth?

Where was the Dream Snatcher's cave?

How did Wanda and Jack get to the cave?

Why was Hypnos stealing people's dreams?

How did Jack and Wanda help him?

What was Mr Jones' worst nightmare?